GREATER LONDON CEMETERIES AND CREMATORIA

compiled by

Patricia S Wolfston

revised by

Clifford Webb

Published by

Society of Genealogists
14 Charterhouse Buildings
Goswell Road
London EC1M 7BA

First Edition, 1982
Second Edition, 1985
Third Edition, 1994

(c) Society of Genealogists, 1982, 1985, 1994

ISBN 0 946789 68 1

CONTENTS

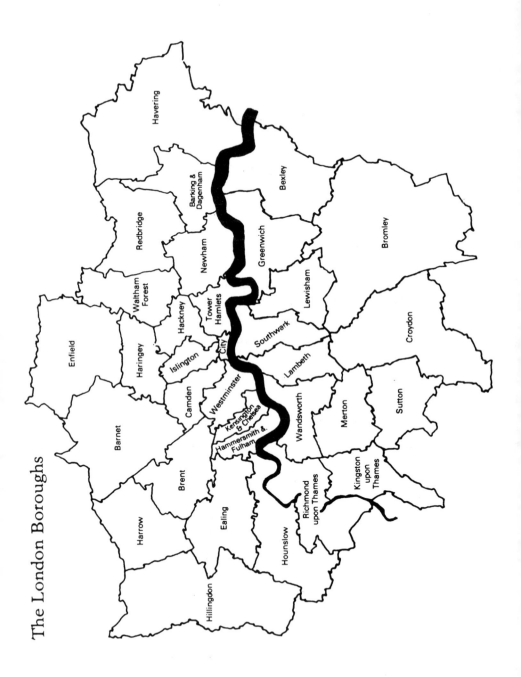

The London Boroughs

Havering

Barking & Dagenham

Bexley

Redbridge

Newham

Greenwich

Bromley

Waltham Forest

Hackney

Tower Hamlets

Lewisham

Enfield

Haringey

Islington

City

Southwark

Croydon

Camden

Westminster

Lambeth

Barnet

Kensington & Chelsea

Wandsworth

Merton

Sutton

Brent

Hammersmith & Fulham

Ealing

Richmond upon Thames

Kingston upon Thames

Harrow

Hounslow

Hillingdon

INTRODUCTION

Locating the burial place of a nineteenth-century resident of the Greater London area is far from an easy task, and the same applies to those who died in this century.

While many burials continued in the local churchyards of the outer London parishes, burials in the inner London churchyards or burial grounds were discontinued at various dates in the 1850s and no parish burial registers were maintained thereafter. Subsequently most burials for inner London took place further away, at non-denominational cemeteries established by either commercial companies or local government bodies.

Exceptions were those established by the Jewish community and the Roman Catholic Church.

THE SEARCH

Some of the following guidelines may prove of value:

1. The deceased of certain areas of London have tended to predominate in certain cemeteries:

> residents of North London in Highgate Cemetery
> residents of East London in Tower Hamlets, Victoria Park and
> Brookwood Cemeteries
> residents of South London in Norwood and Nunhead Cemeteries
> residents of West London in Kensal Green Cemetery.

2. Economic status could affect the location of burial. Brookwood Cemetery and others competed to undertake contracts tendered each year by several London boroughs for the burial of their poor. Although out of the Greater London Council area, Brookwood probably buried half of East London and to facilitate this Waterloo Station had a special casket-loading platform.

3. The St Marylebone Cemetery catered for the affluent middle classes of Marylebone, Highgate and Hampstead, with a high proportion also in the professional and military occupations.

4. Certain parishes bought parcels of newly established cemeteries: St George Hanover Square at Hanwell, and St Anne Soho, St Margaret and St John Westminster at Brookwood. At Norwood an area was reserved for the brotherhood of the Greek community in London.

5. Foremost amongst the burial grounds devoted especially to Dissenters was Bunhill Fields and afterwards Abney Park Cemetery. For those who were Quakers it would be advisable to undertake the search at the library of the Religious Society of Friends, Friends House, Euston Road, London NW1 (Tel. 071-387 3601).

6. Just as the names of the registration districts used by the General Register Office (St Catherine's House) keep changing so do those of the cemeteries. As ownership changes, so do some of the names, although obviously not the location; hence if encountering difficulty it is wise to check for similarity of address.

BEFORE CONTACTING A REPOSITORY

Not all registers contain indexes and in some cases where they exist they are for owners of grave plots rather than individuals interred there. Therefore it is strongly recommended that the appropriate date of death be ascertained prior to making any contact with a source listed below.

Where it has been indicated that a member of the public MAY NOT undertake the search, we have been requested to provide:

    the name of the deceased
    the approximate date of death
    the reason the information is being requested.

Since some repositories charge a fee, do not be surprised if that proves to be the case with the one you approach.

Where it has been indicated that a member of the public may undertake the search, it is recommended that an appointment be requested a minimum of 24 hours in advance. Many of these places are primarily engaged in the planning of present-day funerals which must obviously take precedence.

For those interested in the history, architectural features, identity of the well-known buried there, or the current physical conditions of a particular cemetery, several books may be consulted. The following provide an excellent introduction:

The London burial grounds, Mrs. Basil Holmes (1896)
London cemeteries, Hugh Meller (1981)
Wate's book of London churchyards, Harvey Hackman (1981)

ACKNOWLEDGEMENTS

The compiler and reviser are indebted to some known and many more unknown individuals all of whom kindly and patiently replied to numerous queries. Graham Bird, Meryl Catty, Susan Lumas, Peter Searle and Elizabeth Silverthorne also lent help in collecting updated details. George Rigal and Charles Tucker supplied information for the Jewish section. Jenny Key prepared the finished product for printing. Despite their co-operation there may still be inaccuracies or omissions; information concerning these will be gratefully received. The cover illustration is based on a photograph in West Norwood Cemetery by Paul Blake.

GEOGRAPHICAL DISTRIBUTION

The Tables are designed to show the geographical area (N-E-S-W-) of all, except the Jewish, burial places considered to be 'local'; i.e. either owned by the governmental unit or physically located in the said area if commercially sponsored.

Reading from left to right, the second column provides the name of the pre-1965 authority formerly in the London County Council (L.C.C.), the old county of Middlesex, or the counties of Essex, Hertfordshire, Kent and Surrey. Column three indicates the 1984 name of the London Borough covering that same area under the Greater London Council. The final column indicates the 'local' cemetery or crematorium and in brackets the date of its first register.

area	pre-1965 authority	present authority	local cemeteries/crematoria
	City of London Corporation	City of London Corporation	Bunhill Fields Burial Ground (1713) City of London Cemetery Little Ilford (1856) City of London Crematorium (1905)
N	Finsbury Islington (L.C.C.)	Islington	Islington Cemetery High Road (1854) Islington Cemetery Cockforsters Road (1960) Islington Crematorium (1937)
N	Hornsey Tottenham Wood Green (Middlesex)	Haringey	Tottenham Cemetery (1856)
N	Edmonton Enfield Southgate (Middlesex)	Enfield	Edmonton Cemetery (1884) Old Southgate Cemetery (c. 1880) Enfield Crematorium (1938) Enfield Lawn Cemetery (1961) Hertford Road Cemetery (1881) Lavender Hill Cemetery (1872) Tottenham Park Cemetery (1912)

area	pre-1965 authority	present authority	local cemeteries/crematoria
NE	Hackney Shoreditch Stoke Newington (L.C.C.)	Hackney	Abney Park Cemetery (Nonconformist; 1840) St Thomas Square Cemetery (1837) Victoria Park Cemetery (1853)
NE	Chingford Leyton Walthamstow (Essex)	Waltham Forest	Chingford Mount Cemetery (1886) Walthamstow Cemetery (1872)
NE	Part of Chigwell Ilford Wanstead & Woodford (Essex)	Redbridge	Barkingside Cemetery (1923) Barkingside Garden of Rest (1953) Buckingham Road Cemetery (1881) Roding Lane Cemetery (1940)
E	Bethnal Green Poplar Stepney (L.C.C.)	Tower Hamlets	Tower Hamlets Cemetery (1841) (see **Introduction** re Brookwood) Gibralter Row Burial Ground (1793)
E	East Ham West Ham (Essex)	Newham	East London Cemetery (1874) Manor Park Cemetery (1874) West Ham Cemetery (1854) Woodgrange Park Cemetery (c. 1909)
E	Barking* Dagenham (Essex)	Barking	Barkingside Cemetery (1923) Chadwell Heath Cemetery (1934) Eastbrook Cemetery (1914) Rippleside Cemetery (1886)

*A very small area formerly in Barking but west of Barking Creek is now in Newham.

area	pre-1965 authority	present authority	local cemeteries/crematoria
E	Hornchurch Romford (Essex)	Havering	Hornchurch Cemetery (1932) Rainham Cemetery (1902) Romford Cemetery (1871) South Essex Crematorium (1950) Upminster Cemetery (1902)
SE	Bermondsey Camberwell Southwark (L.C.C.)	Southwark	Camberwell Cemetery (1856) Camberwell New Cemetery (1927) Honor Oak Crematorium (1939) Nunhead Cemetery (1840)

area	pre-1965 authority	present authority	local cemeteries/crematoria
SE	Greenwich Woolwich* (L.C.C.)	Greenwich	Charlton Cemetery (1864) Eltham Cemetery (1935) Greenwich Cemetery (1856) Plumstead Cemetery (1890) Royal Hospital Cemetery (Navy; 1848) Woolwich Cemeteries (1856, 1885)

*Two very small enclaves north of the Thames, formerly in Woolwich, are now in Newham.

SE	Deptford Lewisham (L.C.C.)	Lewisham	Brockley Cemetery (1858) Grove Park Cemetery (1935) Hither Green Cemetery (1873) Ladywell Cemetery (1858) Lewisham Crematorium (1956)
SE	Bexley Crayford Part of Chisle-hurst & Sidcup Erith (Kent)	Bexley	Bexleyheath Cemetery (1879) Erith Cemetery (1894) Sidcup Cemetery (1912)
SE	Beckenham Bromley Part of Chisle-hurst & Sidcup Orpington Penge* (Kent)	Bromley	Beckenham Cemetery (1876) Beckenham Crematorium (1956) Biggin Hill Cemetery (1937) Bromley Hill Cemetery (1907) Chislehurst Cemetery (1912) London Road Cemetery (1877) Plaistow Cemetery (1892) St Luke's Cemetery (1894) St Mary Cray Cemetery (1884)

*Prior to 1965 Penge was administratively part of Bromley, Kent. It was formerly in Surrey.

S	Croydon Coulsdon & Purley (Surrey)	Croydon	Croydon Cemetery (1897) Croydon Crematorium (1937) Greenlawn Memorial Park (1940) Queen's Road Cemetery (1861)
SW	Lambeth Part of Wandsworth (i.e.Clapham & Streatham) (L.C.C.)	Lambeth	Lambeth Cemetery (1854) Streatham Cemetery (1893) West Norwood Cemetery (1837) West Norwood Crematorium (1915)

area	pre-1965 authority	present authority	local cemeteries/crematoria
SW	Battersea Wandsworth (except for Clapham & Streatham area) (L.C.C.)	Wandsworth	Battersea St Mary's Cemetery (1860) Putney Lower Common Cemetery (1855) Putney Vale Cemetery (1891) Wandsworth Cemetery (1878) Morden Cemetery (Battersea New Cemetery) (1892) North East Surrey Crematorium (1958)
SW	Merton & Morden Mitcham Wimbledon (Surrey)	Merton	Merton & Sutton Joint Cemetery (1947) Mitcham Cemetery, Church Road (1883) Mitcham Cemetery, London Road (1929) South London Crematorium (1936) Streatham Cemetery (1893) Streatham Park Cemetery (1911) Wimbledon Cemetery (1876)
SW	Beddington & Wallington Carshalton Sutton & Cheam (Surrey)	Sutton	Bandon Hill Cemetery (1899) Cuddington Cemetery (1902) Sutton Cemetery (1889)
SW	Barnes Richmond-upon-Thames (Surrey) Twickenham (Middlesex)	Richmond-upon-Thames	East Sheen Cemetery (1906) Hampton Cemetery (1859) Mortlake Crematorium (1939)[1] Old Mortlake Cemetery (1887) Richmond Cemetery (1894) South West Middlesex Crematorium (1954)[2] Teddington Cemetery (1879) Twickenham Cemetery (1867)
SW	Kingston-upon-Thames Malden & Coombe Surbiton	Kingston-upon-Thames	Kingston Cemetery (1855) Kingston Crematorium (1952) Surbiton Cemetery (1915)

1. Mortlake Crematorium is jointly owned by Ealing, Hammersmith, Hounslow and Richmond.
2. South West Middlesex Crematorium is jointly owned by Ealing, Hillingdon, Hounslow, Richmond and Spelthorne.

area	pre-1965 authority	present authority	local cemeteries/crematoria
W	Fulham Hammersmith (L.C.C.)	Hammersmith & Fulham	Brompton Cemetery (1840) Fulham Cemetery (1865) Hammersmith Cemetery (1869) Hammersmith New Cemetery (1926) Part of Kensal Green (All Souls) Cemetery (1833) Mortlake Cemetery (1926)[3] Mortlake Crematorium (1939) North Sheen Cemetery (1905) West London Crematorium (1939)
W	St Marylebone Paddington City of Westminster (L.C.C.)	City of Westminster	Paddington New Cemetery, Milespit Hill (1937) Paddington Cemetery, Willesden Lane (1855) St Marylebone Cemetery (1855) St Marylebone Crematorium (1938) Westminster Cemetery (1854) (see **Introduction** re certain parishes)
W	Chelsea Kensington (L.C.C.)	Royal Borough of Kensington & Chelsea	Gunnersbury Cemetery (1929) Part of Kensal Green (All Souls) Cemetery (1833) Kensington Hanwell Cemetery (1855) Royal Hospital Chelsea Burial Ground (Army; 1692)
W	Acton Ealing Southall (Middlesex)	Ealing	Acton Cemetery (1895) Greenford Park Cemetery (1901) Hanwell Cemetery (1854) Havelock Road Cemetery (1883) Hortus Road Cemetery (1944) Mortlake Crematorium (1939)[4] South Ealing Cemetery (1861) South West Middlesex Crematorium (1954)[5]

3. see note 1.
4. see note 1.
5. see note 2.

area	pre-1965 authority	present authority	local cemeteries/crematoria
W	Brentford & Chiswick Heston & Isleworth (Middlesex)	Hounslow	Bedfont Cemetery (1941) Borough Cemetery (1942) Chiswick New Cemetery (1933) Chiswick Old Cemetery (1888) Feltham Cemetery (1886) Hatton Cemetery (1974) Hounslow Cemetery (1869) Isleworth Cemetery (1880) Mortlake Crematorium (1939)[6] New Brentford Cemetery (1903) South West Middlesex Crematorium (1954)[7]
W	Hayes & Harlington Ruislip - Northwood Uxbridge Yiewsley & West Drayton (Middlesex)	Hillingdon	Breakspear Crematorium (1958)[8] Cherry Lane Cemetery (1937) Harlington Burial Ground (1871) Harmondsworth Cemetery (1905) Hillingdon & Uxbridge Cemetery (1856) Northwood Cemetery (1915) South West Middlesex Crematorium (1954)[9] Victoria Lane Burial Ground (1871) West Drayton Cemetery (1939)
NW	Hampstead Holborn St Pancras (L.C.C.)	Camden	Hampstead Cemetery (1876) Highgate Cemetery (1839) St Pancras Cemetery (1854)
NW	Wembley Willesden (Middlesex)	Brent	Alperton Cemetery (1917) Carpenders Park Cemetery (1954) Wembley Old Burial Ground (1867) Willesden New Cemetery (1893) Willesden Old Cemetery (1868)
NW	Harrow Middlesex	Harrow	Breakspear Crematorium (1958)[10] Eastcote Lane Cemetery (1922) Harrow Cemetery (1888) Harrow Weald Cemetery (1937) Paines Lane Cemetery (1860s) Pinner New Cemetery (1933) Roxeth Hill Burial Ground (1922) Wealdstone Cemetery (1902)

6. see note 1.
7. see note 2.
8. Breakspear Crematorium is jointly owned by Harrow and Hillingdon.
9. see note 2.
10. see note 8.

area	pre-1965 authority	present authority	local cemeteries/crematoria
NW	Barnet East Barnet (Herts) Finchley Friern Barnet Hendon (Middlesex)	Barnet	East Finchley Cemetery (1855) Golders Green Crematorium (1903) Great Northern London Cemetery (1861) Hendon Cemetery (1899) Hendon Crematorium (1922)

MIDDLESEX EXCLUDED FROM GREATER LONDON

	Potters Bar	Hertsmere, Herts.	Allum Lane Lawn Cemetery (1962)
	Staines Sunbury-on- Thames	Spelthorne, Surrey	Ashford Cemetery (1910) South West Middlesex Crematorium (1954) Staines Cemetery (1913) Stanwell Burial Ground (1900) Sunbury Cemetery (1900)

OUTSIDE GREATER LONDON AREA

Brookwood Cemetery, Woking, Surrey (1854)

NON-DENOMINATIONAL CEMETERIES AND CREMATORIA: ALPHABETICAL LISTING

Name & address of cemetery	Location of burial registers	Date registers begin	Can you yourself search
Abney Park Cemetery Stoke Newington High Street, London N16 Tel. 071-275 9443	Springfield Park Mansion, Springfield, London E5. Microfilm 1840-1978 at Hackney Archives Dept., Rose Lipman Library (Hackney), 43 De Beauvoir Road, London N1 5SQ Tel. 071-294 0118	1840	Yes
Acton Cemetery Park Royal Road, London W3 6XB	The Cemetery Office, The London Borough of Ealing, Perceval House, 14/16 Uxbridge Road, London W5 2HL Tel. 081-758 5625	1895	Yes (£38.50 search fee)
All Saints Cemetery	see Nunhead		
All Souls Cemetery	see Kensal Green		
Allum Lane Lawn Cemetery Allum Lane, Borehamwood, Herts.	Hertsmere Borough Council Civic Offices, Elstree Way, Borehamwood, Herts. WD6 1WA Tel. 081-207 2277	1962	No
Alperton Cemetery Clifford Road, Alperton, Wembley, Middlesex	Cemeteries Office, Clifford Road, Alperton, Wembley, Middlesex HA0 1AF Tel. 081-902 2385	1917	No
Ashford Cemetery Long Lane, Ashford, Middlesex	Borough of Spelthorne Council Offices, Knowle Green, Staines, Middlesex TW18 1XB Tel. 0784-252538	1910	No
Bandon Hill Cemetery Plough Lane, Beddington, Surrey	at the Cemetery	1899	No

Name & address of cemetery	Location of burial registers	Date registers begin	Can you yourself search
Barkingside Cemetery Longwood Gardens, Barkingside, Ilford, Essex	Longwood Gardens Tel. 081-478 3020 x 5013	1923	No
Barkingside Garden of Rest Longwood Gardens, Barkingside, Ilford, Essex	Longwood Gardens Tel. 081-478 3020 x 5013	1953	No
Battersea New Cemetery	see Morden Cemetery		
Battersea St Mary's Cemetery	as for Wandsworth Cemetery	1860	No
Beckenham Cemetery Elmers End Road, Beckenham, Kent BR3 4TD	at the Cemetery Tel. 081-650 9290 or 0322	1876	Yes
Beckenham Crematorium Elmers End Road, Beckenham, Kent BR3 4TD	at Beckenham Cemetery Tel. 081-650 9290 or 0322	1956	Yes
Becontree Cemetery	see Eastbrook Cemetery		
Bedfont Cemetery Bedfont Road, Feltham, Middlesex	Civic Centre, London Borough of Hounslow, Lampton Road, Hounslow, Middlesex TW3 4DN Tel. 081-570 7728 (Cemetery Section)	1941	Yes
Bexleyheath Cemetery Banks Lane, Broadway, Bexleyheath, Kent	The Local Studies Centre, Bexley Libraries and Museums Dept., Hall Place, Bourne Road, Bexley, Kent DA5 1PQ Tel. 0322-526574 x 217/8 Registers from 1944 at the Cemetery (London Borough of Bexley Cemetery Dept., 6 Gravel Hill, Bexleyheath, Kent DA6 7PN Tel. 081-303 7777 x 8484)	1879	Yes; from 1944 No

Name & address of cemetery	Location of burial registers	Date registers begin	Can you yourself search
Biggin Hill Cemetery Kingsmead Avenue, Biggin Hill, Kent	Cemeteries Section, Department of Leisure Services, Central Library, High Street, Bromley, Kent BR1 1EX Tel. 081-313 4413	1937	Yes
Borough Cemetery Powder Mill Lane, Twickenham, Middlesex	as for Bedfont Cemetery	1942	Yes
Breakspear Crematorium Breakspear Road, Ruislip, Middlesex HA4 7SJ	at the Crematorium Tel. 0895-632843	1958	Yes
Brockley Cemetery Ladywell Road, London SE13	Lewisham Crematorium and Cemetery Services, Verdant Lane, Catford, London SE6 1TP Tel. 081-698 4955	1858	No
Bromley Hill Cemetery Bromley Hill, Bromley, Kent	as for Biggin Hill Cemetery	1907	Yes
Brompton Cemetery Fulham Road, London SW10 9UG	at the Cemetery Tel. 071-352 1201	1840	No
Brookwood Cemetery Cemetery Pales, Brookwood, Woking, Surrey GU24 0BL	at the Cemetery Tel. 0483-472222 Copy registers 1854-1978 at Surrey Record Office, County Hall, Penrhyn Road, Kingston-upon-Thames KT1 2DN	1854	No
Buckingham Road Cemetery (formerly known as Great Ilford Cemetery) Buckingham Road, Ilford, Essex	as Barkingside Cemetery Tel. 081-478 3020 x 5013	1881	No

Name & address of cemetery	Location of burial registers	Date registers begin	Can you yourself search
Bunhill Fields Burial Ground City Road, London EC1	1713-1854 indexes at Public Record Office, Chancery Lane, London WC2 (RG 4/4652-4657); 1789-1854 interment order books and transcripts of inscriptions (Ms 1092): 18 vols at Guildhall Library, Aldermanbury, London EC2; 1823-54 index to books of interment at Society of Genealogists Library		Yes Yes Yes
Camberwell New Cemetery Brenchley Gardens, London SE23 3RD	at the Cemetery Tel. 071-639 3121	1927	Yes
Camberwell Old Cemetery Forest Hill Road, London SE22	Camberwell New Cemetery Office, Brenchley Gardens, London SE23 3RD Tel. 071-639 3121	1856	Yes
Carpenders Park Cemetery Oxhey Lane, Carpenders Park, Nr.Watford, Herts.	as for Alperton Cemetery	1954	No
Chadwell Heath Cemetery Whalebone Lane North, Dagenham, Essex	as for Rippleside Cemetery	1934	Yes
Charlton Cemetery Cemetery Lane, London SE7	at the Cemetery and also at London Borough of Greenwich Cemeteries Department, Town Hall, Wellington Street, Woolwich, London SE18 Tel. 081-854 8888 x 5011	1864	Yes - two days notice
Cherry Lane Cemetery Shepiston Lane, Harlington, Middlesex	Cemeteries Department, Civic Centre, High Street, Uxbridge, Middlesex Tel. 08952-50111 x 2382/3	1937	No

Name & address of cemetery	Location of burial registers	Date registers begin	Can you yourself search
Chingford Mount Cemetery Old Church Road, London E4 6ST	at the Cemetery Tel. 081-524 5030 Some registers at Waltham Forest Archives, Vestry House Museum, Vestry Road, London E17	1886	No
Chislehurst Cemetery Beaverwood Road, Chislehurst, Kent	as for Biggin Hill Cemetery	1912	Yes
Chiswick New Cemetery Staveley Road, London W4 2SJ	part at Cemetery; part at Civic Centre, London Borough of Hounslow, Lampton Road, Hounslow, Middlesex TW3 4DN Tel. 081-570 7728 (Cemetery Section)	1933	Yes
Chiswick Old Cemetery Corney Road, London W4	as for Chiswick New Cemetery Tel. 081-995 6326	1888	Yes
City of London and Tower Hamlets	see Tower Hamlets Cemetery		
City of London Cemetery Aldersbrook Road, Manor Park, London E12 5DQ	original register 1856-date at Cemetery; copy 1856-1915 at Guildhall Library, Aldermanbury, London EC2 (Ms 10,445) 61 vols	1856	Yes
City of London Crematorium Aldersbrook Road, Manor Park, London E12 5DQ	City of London Cemetery, Aldersbrook Road, Manor Park, London E12 5DQ	1905	Yes
City of Westminster Cemetery	see Hanwell Cemetery		
Crow Lane Cemetery	see Romford Cemetery		
Croydon Cemetery Mitcham Road, Croydon, Surrey CR9 3AT	at the Cemetery Tel. 081-684 3877	1897	Yes

Name & address of cemetery	Location of burial registers	Date registers begin	Can you yourself search
Croydon Crematorium Mitcham Road, Croydon, Surrey CR9 3AT	at Croydon Cemetery	1937	Yes
Crystal Palace District Cemetery	see Beckenham Cemetery		
Cuddington Cemetery Lindsey Road, Worcester Park, Sutton, Surrey	Sutton Cemetery, Alcorn Close, Sutton, Surrey SM3 9PX Tel. 081-644 9437	1902	No
Deptford Cemetery	see Brockley Cemetery		
Ealing & Old Brentford Cemetery	see South Ealing Cemetery		
Eastbrook Cemetery The Chase, off Dagenham Road, Dagenham, Essex	as for Rippleside Cemetery	1914	Yes
Eastcote Lane Cemetery Eastcote Lane, South Harrow, Middlesex HA2 8RN	Cemetery Office, Harrow Weald Cemetery, Clamp Hill, Stanmore, Middlesex HA7 3JS Tel. 081-954 1561	1922	No
East Finchley Cemetery (formerly St Marylebone Cemetery), East End Road, East Finchley, London N2 9AG	see Hanwell Cemetery 38 Uxbridge Road, London W7 3PP Tel. 081-567 0913 see also Islington & St Pancras Cemeteries	1855	Yes
East London Cemetery Grange Road, Plaistow, London E13 0HB	at the Cemetery	1874	No
East Sheen Cemetery Sheen Road, Richmond, Surrey TW10 5BJ	London Borough of Richmond Cemeteries Office, East Sheen Cemetery, Sheen Road, Richmond, Surrey TW10 5BJ Tel. 081-876 4511	1906	No

Name & address of cemetery	Location of burial registers	Date registers begin	Can you yourself search
Edmonton Cemetery Church Street, London N9	part at Cemetery; part at Cemetery Department, The Civic Centre, Enfield, Middlesex Tel. 081-366 6565	1884	Yes
Elmers End Cemetery	see Beckenham Cemetery		
Eltham Cemetery Rochester Way, London SE9	as for Charlton Cemetery	1935	Yes
Enfield Cemetery	see Hertford Road Cemetery & Lavender Hill Cemetery		
Enfield Crematorium Great Cambridge Road, Enfield, Middlesex EN1 4DS	at the Crematorium Tel. 081-363 8324	1938	No; index Yes
Enfield Lawn Cemetery Enfield Crematorium, Great Cambridge Road, Enfield, Middlesex EN1 4DS	Enfield Crematorium Tel. 081-363 8324	1961	Yes
Erith Cemetery Brook Street, Erith, Kent	as for Bexleyheath Cemetery. Registers from 1963 at the Cemetery (London Borough of Bexley Cemetery Dept., 6 Gravel Hill, Bexleyheath, Kent DA6 7PN Tel. 081-303 7777 x 8484)	1894	Yes; from 1963 No
Feltham Cemetery Sunbury Road, Feltham, Middlesex TW13	as for Bedfont Cemetery Tel. 081-890 1912	1886	Yes
Fulham Cemetery Fulham Palace Road, London SW6 3LA	Parks & Cemetery Department, London Borough of Hammersmith & Fulham, Pryors Bank, Bishop's Park, London SW6 3LA Tel. 071-736 7181	1865	No
Gibraltar Row Burial Ground Bethnal Green	at the Public Record Office, Chancery Lane, London WC2 (RG 8/305-314); indexed transcript on open shelves	1793- 1826	Yes

Name & address of cemetery	Location of burial registers	Date registers begin	Can you yourself search
Golders Green Crematorium Hoop Lane, London NW11 7NL	at the Crematorium Tel. 081-455 2374	1903	No
Great Northern London Cemetery (now New Southgate Cemetery) Brunswick Park Road, London N11 1JJ	at the Cemetery Tel. 081-361 1713	1861	No
Greenford Park Cemetery Windmill Lane, Greenford, Middlesex UB6 9DU	as for Acton Cemetery	1901	Yes (£38.50 search fee)
Greenlawn Memorial Park Chelsham, Warlingham, Surrey CR6 9EQ	Croydon Cemetery, Mitcham Road, Croydon, Surrey CR9 3AT Tel. 081-684 3877	1940	Yes
Greenwich Cemetery Well Hall Road, London SE9	as for Charlton Cemetery	1856	Yes
Greenwich Hospital Burial Ground	see Royal Hospital Cemetery		
Grove Park Cemetery Marvels Lane, Lee, London SE12	Lewisham Crematorium & Cemetery Services, Verdant Lane, Catford, London SE6 1TP Tel. 081-698 4955	1935	No
Gunnersbury Cemetery Gunnersbury Avenue, London W3 8LE	at the Cemetery Tel. 081-992 2924	1929	No
Hammersmith Cemetery Margravine Road, London W6	as for Fulham Cemetery	1869	No
Hammersmith New Cemetery Clifford Avenue, London SW14	as for Fulham Cemetery	1926	No

Name & address of cemetery	Location of burial registers	Date registers begin	Can you yourself search
Hampstead Cemetery Fortune Green Road, London NW6 1DR	at the Cemetery Tel. 071-435 6142	1876	No
Hampton Cemetery Broad Lane, Hampton, Middlesex	as for Twickenham Cemetery	1859	No
Hanwell Cemetery (formerly known as City of Westminster Cemetery) 38 Uxbridge Road, London W7 3PP	at the Cemetery Tel. 081-567 0913	1854	Yes - phone before
Harlington Burial Ground St Peter's Way, Harlington, Middlesex	as for Cherry Lane Cemetery	1871	No
Harmondsworth Cemetery High Street, Harmondsworth Village, Middlesex	as for Cherry Lane Cemetery	1905	No
Harrow Cemetery Pinner Road, Harrow, Middlesex HA1 4JA	Harrow Weald Cemetery, Clamp Hill, Stanmore, Middlesex HA7 3JS Tel. 081-954 1561	1888	No
Harrow Weald Cemetery Clamp Hill, Stanmore, Middlesex HA7 3JS	at the Cemetery Tel. 081-954 1561	1937	No
Hatton Cemetery Faggs Road, Feltham, Middlesex	as for Bedfont Cemetery	1974	Yes
Havelock Road Cemetery Church Road, Southall, Middlesex UB2 4NT	as for Acton Cemetery	1883	Yes (£38.50 search fee)
Hendon Cemetery Holders Hill Road, London NW7 1NB	at the Cemetery	1899	Yes

Name & address of cemetery	Location of burial registers	Date registers begin	Can you yourself search
Hendon Crematorium Holders Hill Road, London NW7 1NB	Hendon Cemetery, Holders Hill Road, London NW7 1NB	1922	Yes
Hertford Road Cemetery Hertford Road, Enfield, Middlesex	as for Old Southgate Cemetery	1881	Yes
Highgate Cemetery Swains Lane, London N6 6PJ Tel. 081-340 1834	Camden Local Studies Library, Holborn Library, Theobalds Road, London WC1X 8PA Tel. 071-413 6342 Also Greater London Record Office, 40 Northampton Road, London EC1 (DL/T/63/1-28) for 1839-71	1839	Yes - phone before
Hillingdon & Uxbridge Cemetery Hillingdon Hill, Hillingdon, Middlesex	as for Cherry Lane Cemetery	1856	No
Hither Green Cemetery Verdant Lane, Catford, London SE6 1TP	Lewisham Crematorium, Verdant Lane, Catford, London SE6 1TP Tel. 081-698 4955	1873	No
Honor Oak Crematorium London SE23 3RD	at the Crematorium Tel. 071-639 7499	1939	Yes
Hornchurch Cemetery Upminster Road, Hornchurch, Essex	Registrar of Cemeteries & Crematoria, South Essex Crematorium, Ockenden Road, Corbets Tey, Upminster, Essex RM14 2UY Tel. 0708-222188	1932	No
Hortus Road Cemetery Merrick Road, Southall, Middlesex UB2 4AU	as for Acton Cemetery	1944	Yes (£38.50 search fee)

Name & address of cemetery	Location of burial registers	Date registers begin	Can you yourself search
Hounslow Cemetery Hanworth Road, Hounslow, Middlesex	as for Bedfont Cemetery	1869	Yes
Isleworth Cemetery Park Road, Isleworth, Middlesex	as for Bedfont Cemetery	1880	Yes
Islington Cemetery High Road, East Finchley, London N2 9AG	at the Cemetery Tel. 081-883 1230	1854	Yes
Islington Cemetery (Trent Park) Cockfosters Road, Barnet, Herts.	as for Islington Cemetery	1960	Yes
Islington Crematorium High Road, London N2 9AG	as for Islington Cemetery	1937	Yes
Kensal Green (All Souls) Cemetery Harrow Road, London W10 4RA	at the Cemetery Tel. 081-969 0152 Also Greater London Record Office, 40 Northampton Road, London EC1 (DL/T/41/1-40) for 1833-72	1833	No
Kensington Hanwell Cemetery Broadway, London W7	Gunnersbury Cemetery, Gunnersbury Avenue, London W4 Tel. 081-992 2924	1855	No
Kingston Cemetery Bonner Hill Road, Kingston-upon-Thames, Surrey KT1 3EZ	at the Cemetery Tel. 081-546 4462	1855	No
Kingston Crematorium Bonner Hill Road, Kingston-upon-Thames, Surrey KT1 3EZ	at the Cemetery & Crematorium Office Tel. 081-546 4462	1952	No
Ladywell Cemetery Ladywell Road, London SE13	Lewisham Cemeteries & Crematorium Services, Verdant Lane, Catford, London SE6 1TP Tel. 081-698 4955	1858	No

Name & address of cemetery	Location of burial registers	Date registers begin	Can you yourself search
Lambeth Cemetery Blackshaw Road, London SW17	Pre-1929 at Archives Department, Minet Library, Knatchbull Road; later registers at the Cemetery Tel. 081-672 1390	1854	Pre- 1929 Yes; later No
Lavender Hill Cemetery Cedar Road, Enfield, Middlesex	as for Old Southgate Cemetery	1872	Yes
Lee Cemetery	see Hither Green Cemetery		
Lewisham Cemetery	see Ladywell Cemetery		
Lewisham Crematorium Verdant Lane, Catford, London SE6 1TP	at the Crematorium Tel. 081-698 4955	1956	No
London Road Cemetery Warner Road, Bromley, Kent	as for Biggin Hill Cemetery	1877	Yes
Manor Park Cemetery Sebert Road, Manor Park, London E7 0NP	at the Cemetery	1874	No
Manor Park Crematorium Sebert Road, Manor Park, London E7 0NP	at Manor Park Cemetery	1955	No
Margravine Road Cemetery	see Hammersmith Cemetery		
Merton and Sutton Joint Cemetery Garth Road, Morden, Surrey	London Borough of Merton, Recreation Division , 9th Floor, Civic Centre, London Road, Morden, Surrey SM4 5DX Tel. 081-545 3666	1947	No
Mill Hill Cemetery (formerly Paddington New Cemetery) Milespit Hill, London NW7	at Hanwell Cemetery	1937	Yes - phone before

Name & address of cemetery	Location of burial registers	Date registers begin	Can you yourself search
Mitcham Cemetery Church Road, Mitcham, Surrey	as for Merton and Sutton Joint Cemetery	1883	No
Mitcham Cemetery London Road, Mitcham, Surrey	as for Merton and Sutton Joint Cemetery	1929	No
Morden Burial Ground South Worple Way and Avenue Gardens, Mortlake, Surrey SW15	see East Sheen Cemetery	1883	No
Morden Cemetery (Battersea New Cemetery) Lower Morden Lane, Morden, Surrey SM4 4NU	Putney Vale Cemetery, Stag Lane, London SW15 3DZ Tel. 081-871 7820/1	1892	No
Mortlake Cemetery Clifford Avenue, London SW14	as for Fulham Cemetery	1926	No
Mortlake Crematorium Kew Meadow Path, Richmond, Surrey TW9 4EM	at the Crematorium Tel. 081-876 8056	1939	Yes
New Brentford Cemetery Sutton Lane, Hounslow, Middlesex	as for Bedfont Cemetery	1903	Yes
New Southgate Cemetery & Crematorium	see Great Northern London Cemetery		
North East Surrey Crematorium Lower Morden Lane, Morden, Surrey SM4 4NU	at the Crematorium Tel. 081-337 4835	1958	No
North Sheen Cemetery Lower Richmond Road, London SW14	as for Fulham Cemetery	1905	No
Northwood Cemetery Chestnut Avenue, Northwood, Middlesex	as for Cherry Lane Cemetery	1915	No

Name & address of cemetery	Location of burial registers	Date registers begin	Can you yourself search
Norwood Cemetery	see West Norwood Cemetery		
Nunhead Cemetery Linden Grove, London SE15	as for Camberwell New Cemetery. Also Greater London Record Office, 40 Northampton Road, London EC1 (DW/T/515-539) for 1842-71	1840	Yes
Oldchurch Cemetery	see Romford Cemetery		
Old Mortlake Cemetery South Worple Way, London SW14	as for East Sheen Cemetery	1887	No
Old Southgate Cemetery Waterfall Road, London N11	Cemetery Department, The Civic Centre, Enfield, Middlesex Tel. 081-366 6565 x 13767 or 081-982 7035	c.1880	Yes
Paddington Cemetery Willesden Lane, London NW6	as for Alperton Cemetery	1855	No
Paddington New Cemetery	see Mill Hill Cemetery		
Paines Lane Cemetery Paines Lane, Pinner, Middlesex HA5 5BP	London Borough of Harrow Cemetery Office, Harrow Weald Cemetery, Clamp Hill, Stanmore, Middlesex HA7 3JS Tel. 081-954 1561	1860s	Yes
Pinner New Cemetery Pinner Road, Pinner, Middlesex	as for Paines Lane Cemetery	1933	No
Plaistow Cemetery Burnt Ash Lane, Bromley, Kent	as for Biggin Hill Cemetery	1892	Yes - phone before
Plumstead Cemetery Wickham Lane, London SE2	as for Charlton Cemetery	1890	Yes

Name & address of cemetery	Location of burial registers	Date registers begin	Can you yourself search
Putney Lower Common Cemetery Mill Hill Road, London SW13	Putney Vale Cemetery, Stag Lane, Putney, London SW15 3DZ Tel. 081-871 7820/1	1855	No
Putney Vale Cemetery Stag Lane, Putney, London SW15 3DZ	at the Cemetery Tel. 081-871 7820/1	1891	No
Queen's Road Cemetery Queen's Road, Croydon, Surrey CRO 2PR	Croydon Cemetery, Mitcham Road, Croydon, Surrey CR9 3AT Tel. 081-684 3877	1861	Yes
Rainham Cemetery Upminster Road North, Rainham, Essex	as for Hornchurch Cemetery	1902	No
Richmond Cemetery Lower Grove Road, Richmond-upon-Thames, Surrey TW10 6HP	Cemeteries Office, East Sheen Cemetery, Sheen Road, Richmond, Surrey TW10 8BJ Tel. 081-876 4511	1894	No
Rippleside Cemetery Ripple Road, Barking, Essex	at the Cemetery Tel. 081-594 2656	1886	Yes
Roding Lane Cemetery Roding Lane North, South Woodford, London E18	Barkingside Cemetery, Longwood Gardens, Barkingside, Ilford, Essex Tel. 081-478 3020 x 5013	1940	No
Romford Cemetery Dagenham Road, Romford, Essex	as for Hornchurch Cemetery. Duplicate set of registers 1888-1953 at Central Library, St Edward's Way, Romford, Essex Tel. 0708-772393/4 Registers from 1871 are being indexed by East of London FHS with a view to publication	1871	No

Name & address of cemetery	Location of burial registers	Date registers begin	Can you yourself search
Roxeth Hill Burial Ground Roxeth Hill, Harrow, Middlesex HA2 0JM	Harrow Weald Cemetery, Clamp Hill, Stanmore, Middlesex HA7 3JS Tel. 081-954 1561	1922	No
Royal Hospital Cemetery (Navy) East Greenwich	Public Record Office, Chancery Lane, London WC2 (RG 8/16-18)	1848-64	Yes
Royal Hospital Chelsea Burial Ground (Army) Royal Hospital Road, London SW3	Public Record Office, Chancery Lane, London WC2 (RG 4)	1692-1856	Yes
St Luke's Cemetery Magpie Hall Lane, Bromley, Kent	as for Biggin Hill Cemetery	1894	Yes - phone before
St Mary Cray Cemetery Star Lane, St Mary Cray, Orpington, Kent	as for Biggin Hill Cemetery	1884	Yes - phone before
St Marylebone Cemetery	see East Finchley Cemetery		
St Marylebone Crematorium East End Road, East Finchley, London N2 9AG	at the Crematorium Tel. 081-346 8973	1938	No
St Pancras Cemetery High Road, East Finchley, London N2 9AG	at the Cemetery Tel. 081-883 1231	1854	Yes
St Thomas Square Cemetery Mare Street, Hackney, London E8	Public Record Office, Chancery Lane, London WC2 (RG 8/41)	1837-76	Yes
Sidcup Cemetery Foots Cray Lane, Sidcup, Kent	as for Bexleyheath Cemetery from 1963. Earlier registers are at The Local Studies Centre, Bexley Libraries and Museums Dept., Hall Place, Bourne Road, Bexley, Kent DA5 1PQ Tel. 0322-526574 x 217/8	1912	No

Name & address of cemetery	Location of burial registers	Date registers begin	Can you yourself search
South Ealing Cemetery South Ealing Road, Ealing, London W5 4QP	as for Acton Cemetery	1861	Yes (£38.50 search fee)
South Essex Crematorium Ockenden Road, Corbets Tey, Upminster, Essex RM14 2UY	at the Crematorium Tel. 0708-222188	1950	No
Southgate Cemetery	see Old Southgate Cemetery		
South London Crematorium Rowan Road, London SW16 5JG	Streatham Park Cemetery, Rowan Road, London SW16 5JG Tel. 081-764 2255	1936	No
South Metropolitan Cemetery	see West Norwood Cemetery		
South West Middlesex Crematorium, Hounslow Road, Hanworth, Feltham, Middlesex TW13 5JH	at the Crematorium Tel. 081-894 9001	1954	No
Staines Cemetery London Road, Staines, Middlesex TW18 4JQ Tel. 0784-452930	Borough of Spelthorne Council Offices, Knowle Green, Staines, Middlesex TW18 1XB Tel. 0784-446307	1913	No
Stanwell Burial Ground Town Lane, Stanwell, Staines, Middlesex	as for Ashford Cemetery	1900	No
Streatham Cemetery Garrat Lane, London SW17 0LT	at the Cemetery Tel. 081-672 1386	1893	No
Streatham Park Cemetery Rowan Road, London SW16 5JG	at the Cemetery Tel. 081-764 2255	1911	No

Name & address of cemetery	Location of burial registers	Date registers begin	Can you yourself search
Sunbury Cemetery Green Way, Sunbury, Middlesex TW16 6NW Tel. 0932-780244	as for Ashford Cemetery	1900	No
Surbiton Cemetery Lower Marsh Lane, Kingston-upon-Thames, Surrey KT1 3BN	Kingston Cemetery, Bonner Hill Road, Kingston-upon-Thames, Surrey KT1 3EZ Tel. 081-546 4462	1915	No
Sutton Cemetery Alcorn Close, Sutton, Surrey SM3 9PX	at the Cemetery Tel. 081-644 9437	1889	No
Teddington Cemetery Shacklegate Lane, Teddington TW11 8SF	as for Twickenham Cemetery	1879	No
Tottenham Cemetery White Hart Lane, Tottenham, London N17	Enfield Crematorium, Great Cambridge Road, Enfield, Middlesex EN1 4DS Tel. 081-363 8324	1856	Yes
Tottenham Park Cemetery Montagu Road, London N9	at the Cemetery Tel. 081-807 1617	1912	Yes
Tottenham & Wood Green Crematorium	see Enfield Crematorium		
Tower Hamlets Cemetery Southern Grove, London E3	Greater London Record Office, 40 Northampton Road, London EC1 1841-1966 (CTHC/1/1-42)	1841	Yes
Trent Park Cemetery	see Islington Cemetery, Cockfosters Road		
Twickenham Cemetery Hospital Bridge Road, Twickenham, Middlesex TW12	Cemeteries Office, East Sheen Cemetery, Sheen Road, Richmond, Surrey TW10 5BJ Tel. 081-876 4511	1867	No

Name & address of cemetery	Location of burial registers	Date registers begin	Can you yourself search
Upminster Cemetery Ockenden Road, Corbets Tey, Upminster, Essex RM14 2UY	as for Hornchurch Cemetery	1902	No
Uxbridge Cemetery	see Hillingdon & Uxbridge Cemetery		
Victoria Lane Burial Ground Victoria Lane, Harlington, Middlesex	as for Cherry Lane Cemetery	1871	No
Victoria Park Cemetery Hackney, London E3	Public Record Office, Chancery Lane, London WC2 (RG 8/42-51)	1853-76	Yes
Walthamstow Cemetery Queen's Road, London E17	Chingford Mount Cemetery, Old Church Road, London E4 6ST Tel. 081-524 5030	1872	No
Wandsworth Cemetery Magdalen Road, London SW18 3NP	Central Cemeteries Office, Putney Vale Cemetery, Stag Lane, Putney, London SW15 3DZ Tel. 081-871 7820/1	1878	No
Wealdstone Cemetery Byron Road, Wealdstone, Harrow, Middlesex	as for Harrow Weald Cemetery	1902	No
Wembley Old Burial Ground High Road, Wembley, Middlesex	as for Alperton Cemetery	1867	Yes - phone before
West Drayton Cemetery Harmondsworth Road, West Drayton, Middlesex	as for Cherry Lane Cemetery	1939	No
West Ham Cemetery Cemetery Road, Forest Gate, London E7 9DE	at the Cemetery Tel. 081-534 1566	1854	Yes
West London and Westminster Cemetery	see Brompton Cemetery		

Name & address of cemetery	Location of burial registers	Date registers begin	Can you yourself search
West London Cemetery	see West Norwood Cemetery		
West London Crematorium Harrow Road, London W10 4RA	as for Kensal Green Cemetery	1939	No
Westminster Cemetery (City of)	see Hanwell Cemetery		
West Norwood Cemetery Norwood Road, London SE27 9JU	at the Cemetery Tel. 081-670 0011 Also Greater London Record Office, 40 Northampton Road, London EC1 (DW/T/899-969) for 1838-1918	1837	No
West Norwood Crematorium Norwood Road, London SE27 9JU	West Norwood Cemetery, Norwood Road, London SE27 9JU	1915	No
Whitton Cemetery	local name for Twickenham Cemetery		
Willesden Lane Cemetery	see Paddington Cemetery		
Willesden New Cemetery Franklyn Road, London NW10	as for Alperton Cemetery	1893	Yes
Willesden Old Cemetery Neasden Lane, London NW1	as for Alperton Cemetery	1868	Yes - phone before
Wimbledon Cemetery Gap Road, London SW19	as for Morden & Sutton Joint Cemetery	1876	No
Woodgrange Park Cemetery Romford Road, London E7	at Badgehurst Ltd., Fen Lane, Orsett, Grays, Essex RM16 3LT Tel. 0375-891440	c.1909	No
Woolwich Cemeteries Kings Highway & Camdale Road, London SE18	as for Charlton Cemetery	1856 & 1885	Yes

RESTRICTED CEMETERIES AND CREMATORIA

Name & address of cemetery	Location of burial registers	Date registers begin	Can you yourself search
ARMY			
Royal Hospital Chelsea Burial Ground London SW3	Public Record Office, Chancery Lane, London WC2 (RG 4)	1692-1856	Yes
NAVY			
Royal Hospital Cemetery East Greenwich	Public Record Office, Chancery Lane, London WC2 (RG 8/16-18)	1848-64	Yes
ROMAN CATHOLIC			
Mortlake Catholic Cemetery North Worple Way, London SW14	St Mary Magdalen, North Worple Way, London SW14 Tel. 081-876 1326	1852	Yes
St Mary's Cemetery Kensal Green, Harrow Road, London NW10 5NU	at the Cemetery Tel. 081-969 1145 Copy, 1858-76, Catholic Family History Society	1858	No
St Patrick's Leytonstone Cemetery Langthorne Road, London E11 4HI	at the Cemetery Tel. 081-539 2451 Copy, 1861-70, & index, 1861-80, Catholic Family History Society	1861	Yes
South London Crematorium Rowan Road, London SW16	although separated into its own physical area there are no separate registers - see above lists for details	1936	No

JEWISH

With this group the important factor is the organization rather than the residential location of the deceased. In the first instance for registers before 1850 apply in writing to the Secretary or Sexton of the appropriate Burial Society.

Union of Orthodox Hebrew Congregations/Adath Yisroel Burial Society, 40 Queen Elizabeth's Walk, Stamford Hill, London N16 0HJ. Tel. 081-802 6262/3

Adath Yisroel Cemetery Carterhatch Lane, Enfield, Middlesex Tel. 081-363 3384	at the Cemetery. see Western Cemetery, Edmonton, for earlier burials	1926	No

Name & address of cemetery	Location of burial registers	Date registers begin	Can you yourself search
Adath Yisroel Cemetery Silver Street, Cheshunt, Herts. Tel. 0707-874572	at the Cemetery. see Burial Society for earlier burials	1964	Yes

Federation of Synagogues Burial Society, 65 Watford Way, London NW4 3AQ. Tel. 081-202 2263

Jewish Cemetery Montagu Road, Angel Road, Lower Edmonton, London N18 Tel. 081-807 2268	at the Cemetery. see Burial Society for earlier burials	1889	No
Rainham Federation Cemetery Upminster Road North, Rainham, Essex	at the Cemetery	1937	No

Spanish and Portuguese Burial Society, 2 Ashworth Road, London W9 1JY. Tel. 071-289 2573

Edgwarebury Cemetery Edgwarebury Lane, Edgware, Middlesex HA8 8LW Tel. 081-958 3388	at the Burial Society	1970s	No
Hoop Lane Cemetery (East Section) Hoop Lane, Golders Green, London NW11 Tel. 081-455 2569	at the Cemetery. see Burial Society for earlier burials	1897	No
Sephardi Neuvo (New) Cemetery 329 Mile End Road, London E1	at the Burial Society	1733	No
Sephardi Velho (Old) Cemetery 253 Mile End Road, London E1	at the Burial Society. Printed in *Misc. Transactions of The Jewish Historical Society of England,* vol.6 (1962)	1657-1742	No

Liberal: Union of Liberal and Progressive Synagogues, Montagu Centre, 21 Maple Street, London W1P 6DS. Tel. 071-580 1663/4

Edgwarebury Cemetery Edgwarebury Lane, Edgware, Middlesex HA8 8LW Tel. 081-958 3388	at the Union Office and the Cemetery	1976	No

Name & address of cemetery	Location of burial registers	Date registers begin	Can you yourself search
Liberal Jewish and Belsize Square Cemetery (to 1979 Union of Progressive Synagogues) Pound Lane, Harlesden Road, Willesden, London NW10 2HG Tel. 081-459 1635	at the Cemetery	1914	Yes
Streatham Park Cemetery (South London Liberal Synagogue) Rowan Road, Streatham Vale, London SW16 5JG Tel. 081-688 1718	at the Cemetery	1915	No

Orthodox: United Synagogue Burial Society, Woburn House, Upper Woburn Place, London WC1H 0EZ. Tel. 071-387 7891. The Society holds a complete set of general indexes for its burial grounds, 1872-1912.

Alderney Road Cemetery Alderney Road, London E1 Tel. 071-790 1445	at the Burial Society	1697-1852	No
Brady Street Cemetery Brady Street, London E1	at the Burial Society	1761-1858	No
Bushey Cemetery Little Bushey Lane, Bushey, Herts. Tel. 081-950 6299	at the Cemetery Office	1947	No
East Ham Cemetery Marlow Road, High Street South, London E6 Tel. 081-472 0554	at the Cemetery Office	1919	No
Hackney Cemetery (formerly Grove Street Cemetery) Lauriston Road, Hackney, London E9 Tel. 081-985 1527	at the Burial Society	1788-1886	No

Name & address of cemetery	Location of burial registers	Date registers begin	Can you yourself search
Hoxton Cemetery Hoxton Street, Hoxton Old Town, London N1	incomplete transcript at the Burial Society (Permanent File No. 919)	1707-1878	No
Jewish Cemetery Cemetery Road, London E7	see West Ham Cemetery		
Plashet Cemetery High Street North, London E12 Tel. 081-472 0525	at East Ham Cemetery Office	1896	No
Waltham Abbey Cemetery Skillet Hill (Honey Lane), Waltham Abbey, Essex Tel. 0992-714492	Superintendent's Office at the Cemetery	1961	No
West Ham Cemetery Buckingham Road, Forest Lane, London E15 Tel. 081-534 3006	at the Burial Society. From 1905 the registers are at Bushey Cemetery	1857	No
Willesden Cemetery Beaconsfield Road, London NW10 Tel. 081-459 0394	Superintendent's Office at the Cemetery	1873	No

Reform Synagogues: West London Synagogue Burial Society, 33 Seymour Place, London W1H 5AT. Tel. 071-723 4404

Name & address of cemetery	Location of burial registers	Date registers begin	Can you yourself search
Balls Pond Cemetery Kingsbury Road, Balls Pond Road, London N1	at the Burial Society	1844-1951	Yes
Edgwarebury Cemetery Edgwarebury Lane, Edgware, Middlesex HA8 8LW Tel. 081-958 3388	at the Spanish and Portuguese Burial Society	1976	Yes
Hoop Lane Cemetery (West Part) Hoop Lane, Golders Green, London NW11 Tel. 081-455 2569	at the Burial Society and the Cemetery	1897	Yes

Name & address of cemetery	Location of burial registers	Date registers begin	Can you yourself search
Jewish Joint Burial Society, Alyth Gardens, Finchley Road, London NW11. Tel. 081-455 8579			
Bullcross Ride Cemetery (Western Cemetery) Cheshunt, Herts. Tel. 0992-717820	West End Great Synagogue, 21 Dean Street, London W1	1968	No
Great Northern London Cemetery (Hendon Reform Synagogue) Brunswick Park Road, London N11	at the Hendon Reform Synagogue, Danescroft Gardens, London NW4 2NA Tel. 081-203 4168/9	1968	Yes
Jewish Cemetery Elmbridge Borough Council Municipal Cemetery, Brooklands Lane, Weybridge, Surrey	Cemetery Office has basic lists; registers are in the Borough Engineer's and Surveyor's Dept., Elmbridge Borough Council, 1 High Street, Esher, Surrey KT10 9RR Tel. 0932-228844	c.1970	Yes
Western Marble Arch Synagogue Burial Society, 32 Great Cumberland Place, London W1H 7DJ. Tel. 071-723 7246			
Bullcross Ride Cemetery (Western Cemetery) Cheshunt, Herts. Tel. 0992-717820	at the Cemetery	1968	No
Western Synagogue Cemetery Montagu Road, Angel Road, Lower Edmonton, London N18 Tel. 081-807 2268	at the Burial Society	1884	No
Western Cemetery Queen's Elm Parade, Fulham Road, Chelsea, London SW3	at the Burial Society. Registers before 1868 destroyed by enemy action	1815-84	Yes- by appoi- ntment
West End Chesed V'Ameth Burial Society, 21 Dean Street, Oxford Street, London W1V 6NE. Tel. 071-437 1873			

Name & address of cemetery	Location of burial registers	Date registers begin	Can you yourself search
Bullcross Ride Cemetery Cheshunt, Herts. Tel. 0992-717820	at the Cemetery Office and Burial Society	1968	No
Rowan Road Cemetery Greyhound Lane, Streatham, London SW16 Tel. 081-764 1566	at the Cemetery. More detailed registers at the Burial Society	1915	No
The Bancroft Road Cemetery (Maiden Lane Synagogue, Westminster), London E1	the registers were destroyed by bombing in 1941	c.1810-1920	